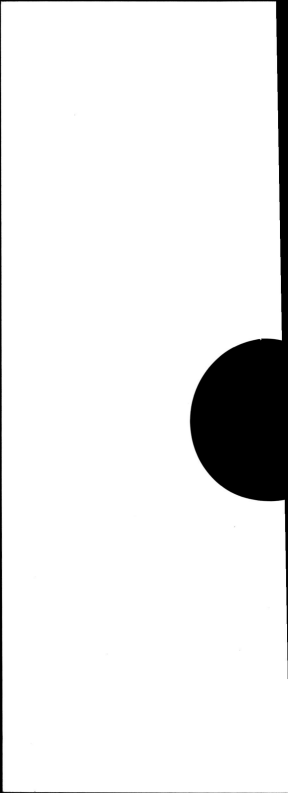

25 CHALLENGES TO DO BEFORE YOU'RE 12

IN QUEST OF ADVENTURE

BY AUSTIN & NICOLA GREGG

ILLUSTRATED BY JOANNE BENT & HILARY MULLEN

First published in Ireland in 2018 by *IN QUEST OF ADVENTURE*

www.inquestofadventure.com
inquestofadventurebook@gmail.com
© *IN QUEST OF ADVENTURE* 2018
ISBN 978-1-5272-2797-2

This book was conceived, designed and produced by *IN QUEST OF ADVENTURE BOOKS*

Authors: Austin and Nicola Gregg

Illustrators: Joanne Bent and Hilary Mullen

Graphic Design: designbytes.ie

Editor: Síne Quinn

Activity collaborators: Finnán, Páidí & Séimí Gregg

Printed in China

Many activities in this book require competent adult supervision. Every effort has been made to ensure that all information in this book is accurate. Neither the publisher nor the authors can be held responsible for any injury, loss or other damages which may result from the use of information in this book.

ABOUT THIS BOOK

This bucket list will captivate your imagination, encourage you to embrace the outdoors and may change your life forever! Take on the challenge and start ticking things off your bucket list now!

★ 25 free, fun, active and accessible challenges to embrace

★ Follow Finn and Ayla through epic adventures

★ Complete each challenge and give the extra activity a go

★ Discover some fascinating facts

★ Capture the moment with an adventure snap or drawing

★ Use the Bucketeer's stickers to track your progress

★ On completion of all challenges you will be a Bucketeer!

★ Enjoy the adventure!

Create childhood memories and cherish them in this keepsake. These 25 challenges are free, fun, active and accessible to all!

Join the revolution, get moving and start living! Become a Bucketeer!

Go for a bike ride, jump in the sea, play hide and seek in the dark, build a den!

To our very own Bucketeers –
Finnán, Páidí & Séimí

ACKNOWLEDGEMENTS

Many thanks to our family, friends and all who have helped to make this book possible. Thanks to Evelyn for all her help and Síne Quinn, Mastermind Ireland for her advice and support. We would especially like to thank Hilary Mullen & Joanne Bent in designbytes.ie, who worked tirelessly to bring the Bucketeers to life!

ABOUT THE AUTHOR

Austin and Nicola Gregg are a husband and wife team with a love of the great outdoors. With over twenty years' experience as primary school teachers, they have seen first-hand the decline in active childhoods and the rise in a sedentary lifestyle.

They live on their family farm with their three boys Finnán (5), Páidí (3) and Séimí (1) in south County Wexford. They are passionate about outdoor living, sport and exploring the world around them.

Austin has many interests including, self-sufficient living, bee-keeping, horticulture, fishing and Irish traditional crafts. He enjoys reading and writing poetry, short stories and plays.

Nicola is extremely active, participating in marathons, triathlons, and adventure racing. The Health Promoting School and Active Flag coordinator in her school, she enjoys instilling a love of healthy living in her school community.

MEET THE BUCKETEERS

ABOUT ME

Name: Finn

Age: 10¾

Height: 1.35m

Weight: 39kg

Friends: Ayla, Zack, Rafik, Conor & Beth

Favourites

Food: Pizza

Drink: Water

Colour: Azure

Hobby: Surfing

Movie: How to Train Your Dragon

Book: Artemis Fowl by Eoin Colfer

Place: Wherever the waves are big!!

Challenge you are most looking forward to:

Bike Ride

Challenge you are least looking forward to:

Minibeast Hunt (yuck!)

Me at Ballybunion Beach, Kerry

ABOUT ME

Name: Ayla

Age: 11 ½

Height: 1.45m

Weight: 37kg

Friends: Finn, Zack, Jasmin & Ciara

Favourites

Food: Spaghetti Bolognese

Drink: Orange juice

Colour: Purple

Hobby: Hiking

Movie: All the Harry Potter Movies

Book: Gangsta Granny by David Walliams

Place: In the mountains

Challenge you are most looking forward to:

Rolling down a hill

Challenge you are least looking forward to:

Crab fishing (ouch!)

Me hiking up Forth Mountain, Wexford

ABOUT ME

Name: _____

Age: _____

Height: _____

Weight: _____

Friends: _____

Favourites

Food: _____

Drink: _____

Colour: _____

Hobby: _____

Movie: _____

Book: _____

Place: _____

Challenge you are most looking forward to:

_____

Challenge you are least looking forward to:

_____

Insert a photo or draw a picture of yourself here

BUCKET LIST

BUILD A DEN

Every Bucketeer needs a headquarters!
So create or find a base with your own rules,
secret entry codes, quick escape routes,
a secret food stash and a lookout for
unwanted vistors!

1

STEPS TO COMPLETION

All you need is a good adventurer's imagination. Look inside and outside for the perfect place.

Look for a secret spot to build your den. Between trees or in hidden corners is always good.

It can be made from anything such as old furniture, boxes, sheets, pallets and plastic covers. Make sure to leave a door and windows.

Plastic sheeting/tarpaulins are good to keep the rain out. Put some on the floor to provide a dry place to sit.

Your den can be covered with branches for camouflage. Find some old chairs or a sofa to make your den as snug as possible.

DID YOU KNOW?

Children in Britain are invited to take part in a sponsored 'Den-Building Day' to raise money to help improve children's lives around the world.

Beavers live in a 'lodge', which is a den made from sticks and mud with underwater entrances.

Black bears give birth and sleep in their dens. Although they sleep in the dens during the winter months, they are not considered true hibernators and may wake occasionally.

 Polar bears will dig snow dens in the autumn. They give birth to their cubs in winter, and they remain in the den until spring.

Lions generally don't live in dens but the female gives birth to her litter of 1-4 cubs in a den.

EXTRA ACTIVITY

Make your own flag to fly over your den and have a secret compartment in your den to hide your possessions.

MAKE A FLAG

Design and make your very own flag to fly over your den. For this activity you will need:

| An old pillowcase | coloured material | marker, glue & scissors | one long stick |

1.

Make a pocket for your flag by applying glue to the edge of your pillowcase. Fold it loosely over the flag pole and remove once completed. Glue the top of the pocket together to allow the flag to sit on the pole.

2.

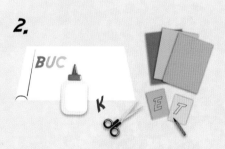

Now for the fun part, decorating your flag! Use a marker to mark out letters or shapes on coloured material. Carefully cut out your designs with a scissors and glue them onto your pillowcase.

3.

Once you have finished decorating your flag you will have to secure it to your flag pole. Simply slip the stick into the pocket you created earlier. Secure it with glue if it feels loose. When dry, secure the flag to the top of your den.

4

ADVENTURE SNAP

Throughout your journal, place a photo of you completing your challenge in this space. Don't have a photo? That's OK, draw a picture of your crazy adventure.

Declaration
of challenge completion

I _____ declare that I have completed this challenege and I'm one step further to becoming a Bucketeer!

Who was with you when you completed this challenge?

_____

_____

_____

What happened during this challenge?

_____

_____

_____

_____

_____

Where did you complete this challenge?

_____

_____

How many stars do you rate this challenege? (Shade them in.)

☆　　☆　　☆　　☆　　☆

Witnessed by

Insert sticker here.

Date

_____   __ /__ /_____

SNAIL RACE

Don't blink or you might miss it! Well, not really, you'll have plenty of time to savour the nail-biting excitement of cheering your snail to the finish line!

STEPS TO COMPLETION

Everyone must find their own snail. They can be found under rotten pieces of wood, on hedgerows, woodlands, pond margins and garden furniture. (Try to pick a fast one!)

Prepare a race track. You will need an old bedsheet or something similar. Stretch it out on a flat surface, draw two circles, an inner and outer and then wet the sheet.

If your snails look very similar, prepare a means to identify your snail (x on shell).

Place your snails in the centre and on the command 'Ready, Steady, Slow!' watch to see which snail makes it to the outer ring first.

Carefully return the competitors to their natural habitat.

DID YOU KNOW?

The practice of rearing snails for food is known as heliciculture.

NORFOLK

The annual "World Snail Racing Championships" started in Norfolk (UK) in the 1960s.

In French cuisine, edible snails are served for dinner.

The 1995 race saw the setting of the benchmark time of two minutes by a snail named 'Archie'.

Snail races begin with the words:'Ready, Steady, Slow!'

EXTRA ACTIVITY

Create a track and see how far your snail can travel in 2 minutes. Calculate its speed!

SNAIL MAZE

This snail is feeling hungry! Can you help and guide him through the maze to his dinner?

Remember to either get your pictures printed for photo evidence of your adventures or draw your own pictures.

ADVENTURE SNAP

Declaration
of challenge completion

I _____ declare that I have completed this challenege and I'm one step further to becoming a Bucketeer!

Who was with you when you completed this challenge?

_____

_____

What happened during this challenge?

_____

_____

_____

_____

Where did you complete this challenge?

_____

_____

How many stars do you rate this challenege? (Shade them in.)

☆ ☆ ☆ ☆ ☆

Witnessed by

Insert sticker here.

Date

_____   __ / __ / ____

CLIMB A TREE

Get a birds-eye view of the world by climbing a tree! To complete this challenge you will need to find a tree that has at least the same amount of branches as your age, i.e. a branch for every year of your life.

STEPS TO COMPLETION

 Make sure you have suitable safe footwear.

 Find a tree with plenty of boughs strong enough to hold your weight.

 Climb one bough at a time making sure you have a firm grip on every one.

 Make sure your feet are secure on sturdy boughs.

 Climb as high as you feel safe and remember to concentrate and be careful on your descent.

DID YOU KNOW?

Trees have been in existence for over 370 million years. They tend to be long-lived, some reaching several thousand years old.

96M   **93M**   **115.6M**

The tallest known tree is a coast Redwood named Hyperion. It stands 115.6m (379ft) high.

 It is estimated that there are over 3 trillion mature trees in the world.

The Oubangui people of west Africa have a tradition of planting a tree when a child is born.

EXTRA ACTIVITY

Retrieve a leaf from the safest highest point you can.

CREATE A LEAF RUBBING

Place a leaf with the bottom side facing up under a sheet of paper. Rub a crayon gently over the paper to reveal the leaf shape. Cut out the leaf rubbing and stick it in the space below.

Stick your leaf rubbing here.

ADVENTURE SNAP

Awesome work Bucketeer, find your next challenge and get ready to explore!

Declaration
of challenge completion

I _____ declare that I have completed this challenege and I'm one step further to becoming a Bucketeer!

Who was with you when you completed this challenge?

_____

_____

_____

What happened during this challenge?

_____

_____

_____

_____

_____

Where did you complete this challenge?

_____

_____

How many stars do you rate this challenege? (Shade them in.)

☆ ☆ ☆ ☆ ☆

Witnessed by

Insert sticker here.

Date

_____   __ /__ /____

HIDE & SEEK IN THE DARK

Are you afraid of the dark? Hide & Seek is great fun at any time but especially when the sun has gone down and you have to depend on all your senses to find your targets.

STEPS TO COMPLETION

This challenge can be completed indoors or outdoors.

One person is the 'Seeker' and everyone else must try to find a good hiding spot.

The 'Seeker' must close their eyes and count to an agreed number while the other players hide.

After reaching this number, the Seeker calls: "Ready or not, here I come!"

The last person to be found becomes the Seeker in the next game.

DID YOU KNOW?

Hide and seek is a game in which any number of players (at least three) conceal themselves in the environment, to be found by one or more seekers.

Bats use a special bio sonar system called "echolocation". This means they find things and their way in the dark by emitting sounds and listening for the echoes.

There is a "Hide and Seek" world championship which is officially named "Nascondino World Championship" (which is Italian for Hide and Seek).

 In Ancient Greece soldiers gained access to the city of Troy by hiding inside a giant wooden horse.

In WWII Anne Frank hid in a secret annex for more than two years to hide from the Nazis.

EXTRA ACTIVITY

Seek and Hide: In this game one person hides and everyone else seeks. When someone discovers the person who is hiding, they hide with them until everyone else has found them.

FIND THE HIDDEN TENS

There are numbers in this puzzle that when you add them up the sum will equal 10. How many 10s can you find?

The numbers must be connected horizontally, vertically or diagonally. The connected numbers go in one direction. Mark the path of the numbers that add up to 10 using a pen or pencil.

4	5	5	6	7	1	7
5	2	9	3	1	9	5
7	2	8	5	7	5	9
7	5	9	8	4	9	6
9	2	4	5	5	6	3
3	5	8	4	6	5	3
2	6	9	8	4	3	3

Soldiers use camouflage to help them hide in combat while many animals use camouflage to evade predators.

CAMELEON

ADVENTURE SNAP

Declaration
of challenge completion

I _____ declare that I have completed this challenege and I'm one step further to becoming a Bucketeer!

Who was with you when you completed this challenge?

_____

_____

_____

What happened during this challenge?

_____

_____

_____

_____

_____

_____

Where did you complete this challenge?

_____

_____

How many stars do you rate this challenege? (Shade them in.)

☆   ☆   ☆   ☆   ☆

Witnessed by   Insert sticker here.   Date

_____   __ / __ / ____

CREATE SEA-SIDE ART

Imagine an art shop with loads of really cool things for free! Well, head to the beach and make use of nature's bounty to create your own masterpiece!

STEPS TO COMPLETION

Comb the beach in search of materials to help you.

Look for shells, driftwood, seaweed, stones, shellfish and any other materials you feel can be used.

Create your masterpiece, which can be anything from your imagination (portraits, animals, space aliens, cool designs, etc.)

Don't forget to frame your picture with sticks, shells, stones or seaweed.

Leave your art for others to enjoy. (Natural materials only!)

DID YOU KNOW?

A seashell is a hard, protective outer layer created by an animal that lives in the sea.

In Western Africa, shell money was legal tender (money) up until the mid 19th century.

The shells are empty because the animal has died and the soft parts have been eaten by another animal or have decayed.

Seaweed is an ingredient in toothpastes, cosmetics and paints.

Seaweed is consumed by many people, especially in Asia. Dillisk and Carrageen moss are popular in Ireland.

EXTRA ACTIVITY

Skim a stone: How many bounces can you do? Flat, smooth stones are the best for skimming, and there are plenty to be found on our beaches. Why not challenge your family and friends to a competition?

MAKE A CRAB FRIDGE MAGNET

Gather some shells at the beach and take them home for some crafty fun! For this activity you will need:

1 shell, paint & paintbrush

googly eyes, glue & pen

2 pipe cleaners & a magnet

a scissors & some card

1. Paint the shell all over and leave it to one side to dry. While waiting take the pipe cleaners and cut them into 10 equal lengths.

2. Place your shell on a piece of card and using a pen, trace around the shell to form a stencil. Using a scissors, carefully cut out the shape.

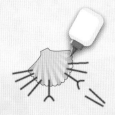

3. Apply glue to the inside of the shell and using the 10 lengths of pipe cleaner, stick 8 legs and 2 pincers to the shell.

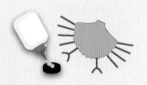

4. Now apply glue around the card cutout you made earlier and stick it to the base of the shell. Glue the magnet to the card once it is securely stuck to the shell.

5. Turn your crab over and add the finishing touches to your creation by gluing on some googly eyes. Once fully dry you can stick this little crab to the fridge door.

28

ADVENTURE SNAP

Here is some sea-side art Ayla and I made earlier, using seaweed, pebbles and framed with driftwood!

Jellyfish by Finn & Ayla

Declaration
of challenge completion

I _____ declare that I have completed this challenege and I'm one step further to becoming a Bucketeer!

Who was with you when you completed this challenge?

_____

_____

What happened during this challenge?

_____

_____

_____

_____

Where did you complete this challenge?

_____

_____

How many stars do you rate this challenege? (Shade them in.)

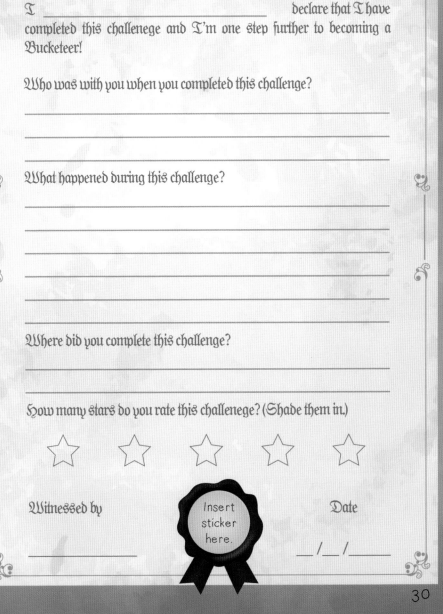

Witnessed by

Insert sticker here.

Date

_____   ___/___/_____

30

CLIMB A HIGH HILL OR MOUNTAIN

'The only way is up'! Keep going till you can't go any higher! On reaching the summit you will be one step closer to becoming a Bucketeer!

STEPS TO COMPLETION

Always go with someone and let others know when you're expected home.

Research to find the safest route and how long it will take.

Wear comfortable footwear such as hiking boots and clothing to suit the weather.

Bring a backpack with suncream, water, snacks, a map, mobile phone and a camera.

At the summit take a well-earned rest and enjoy the view.

DID YOU KNOW?

A mountain is usually defined as any summit at least 610 metres above sea level.

The highest mountain on Earth is Mount Everest in the Himalayas of Asia, whose summit is 8,850 m.

MOUNT EVEREST

8,850 M

The distinction between a hill and a mountain is unclear and largely subjective, but a hill is universally considered to be less tall and less steep than a mountain.

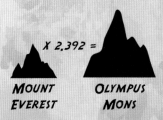

MOUNT EVEREST X 2.392 = **OLYMPUS MONS**

The highest known mountain on any planet in the Solar System is Olympus Mons on Mars at 21,171 m. It is actually a large shield volcano.

EXTRA ACTIVITY

On reaching the summit try to spot some well-known local landmarks (e.g a church spire, village or town).

MEMORY GAME

Take 30 seconds to examine the contents of Ayla's backpack and see if you can answer all of Finn's questions on the next page!

34

Can you remember how many pieces of fruit Ayla had packed in her backpack? What factor sun cream she took with her? How about the direction the compass was pointed? Can you name the remaining items she brought with her?

ADVENTURE SNAP

Declaration
of challenge completion

I _____ declare that I have completed this challenege and I'm one step further to becoming a Bucketeer!

Who was with you when you completed this challenge?

_____
_____

What happened during this challenge?

_____
_____
_____
_____

Where did you complete this challenge?

_____
_____

How many stars do you rate this challenege? (Shade them in.)

☆ ☆ ☆ ☆ ☆

Witnessed by   Insert sticker here.   Date

_____   __ /__ /____

36

MINIBEAST HUNT

Let's go on an expedition to observe 'creepy-crawlies' in their natural habitat. Delve into a forest of grass and upturn rocks to reveal the secrets of the 'Minibeast Kingdom'.

You will need an empty, clean jar to collect your minibeasts.

Look under wood/stones and examine the underside of leaves to find your mini beasts and put them into your jar.

Get down on your belly, pick a spot in the grass and look as closely as you can into the grass until you find a minibeast.

Use a magnifying glass to get a 'close up' of your find.

Before returning your 'little critters', investigate how many legs, antennae, eyes and wings they have.

DID YOU KNOW?

'Minibeast' is a small invertebrate animal, including spiders, ants, butterflies, bees, wasps, flies, woodlice and many others.

Ladybirds have yellow blood which they release when they sense danger.

An arthropod is an invertebrate (no spine) animal having an exoskeleton (external skeleton), a segmented body, and jointed appendages.

The collective name for a group of butterflies is called a 'kaleidoscope' of butterflies.

Earthworms eat their own weight in soil and organic matter everyday and poo out the same amount.

EXTRA ACTIVITY

Try to gently catch a butterfly in a net, identify it and remember to release it afterwards.

FIND THE MATCHING PAIR

Only two of these butterfly shapes are exactly the same. See if you can spot them! When you do, put a circle around the two identical ones.

ADVENTURE SNAP

BUCKETEER CODE
- Explore with care
- Be gentle with animals
- Do not disturb habitats
- Where possible, observe
  rather than handle
- Return animals to their
  habitats ASAP

41

Declaration
of challenge completion

I _____ declare that I have completed this challenege and I'm one step further to becoming a Bucketeer!

Who was with you when you completed this challenge?

_____

_____

What happened during this challenge?

_____

_____

_____

_____

Where did you complete this challenge?

_____

_____

How many stars do you rate this challenege? (Shade them in.)

☆ ☆ ☆ ☆ ☆

Witnessed by

Insert sticker here.

Date

_____   __ / __ / ____

RACE LEAVES DOWN A STREAM

Bobbing over rocks and racing over rapids, watch as your 'boat' takes on the challenge to be the winner in this aquatic rollercoaster ride! Ask an adult to come along for this challenge as water always poses a danger.

STEPS TO COMPLETION

You will need some leaves (or sticks).

Find a way to remember which leaf is yours.
(Note colour, size and shape.)

Pick a starting and a finishing point.

On a command everyone must place their leaves
in the water at the same time and in a straight
line.

The winner is the person whose leaf first
passes the finishing point.

DID YOU KNOW?

An alternative to racing leaves is to race sticks (called Pooh Sticks!)

Poohsticks is a sport first mentioned in a Winnie-the-Pooh book by A. A. Milne.

The annual World Poohsticks Championships have been held at Days Lock on the River Thames in the UK since 1984.

Canada is the only country in the world to have a leaf on its flag.

Leaves float on water because they have a lower density than water.

EXTRA ACTIVITY

Try to see can your leaf carry a passenger (a small stick or pebble).

LETTER SCRAMBLE

Cross off the letters that appear more than once then rearrange the remaining letters to find the mystery words. Clue : countries!

MYSTERY WORD 1

MYSTERY WORD 2

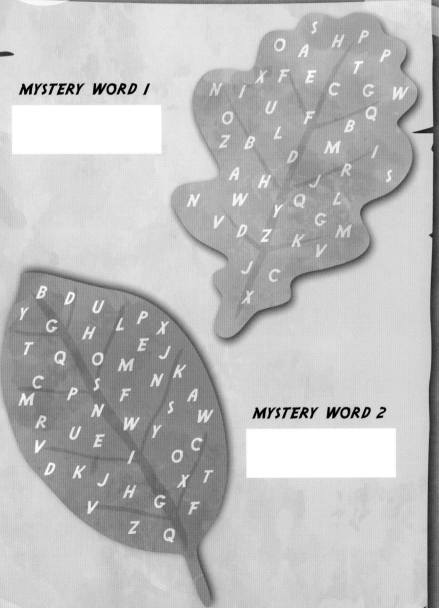

Did you see any of these creatures on this adventure? A fish, a duck, a heron or a frog?

ADVENTURE SNAP

Declaration
of challenge completion

I _____ declare that I have completed this challenge and I'm one step further to becoming a Bucketeer!

Who was with you when you completed this challenge?

_____
_____

What happened during this challenge?

_____
_____
_____
_____
_____

Where did you complete this challenge?

_____
_____

How many stars do you rate this challenge? (Shade them in.)

☆ ☆ ☆ ☆ ☆

Witnessed by   Date

Insert sticker here.

_____   __ /__ /____

CYCLING ADVENTURE

Ok Bucketeer, jump up on your bike, get ready to steer and whether you go far or near, make sure to put on your safety gear!

STEPS TO COMPLETION

Get an adult to accompany you on this adventure.

Check that your tyres are inflated and your brakes are properly working.

Before you go know the Rules of the Road and wear safety gear (helmet, lights and hi-viz).

Bring a small backpack with a rain-jacket, drink, map, some snacks and a camera.

Keep track of where you are going so you'll know how to get home.

DID YOU KNOW?

Bicycles were introduced in the 19th century and now number approximately one billion worldwide.

A bike built for two is called a 'Tandem bicycle'.

The Tour de France is the world's most famous bicycle race.

Fred A. Birchmore circled the globe by bike in 1935. He cycled 40,233km and wore out 7 sets of tyres.

BMX stands for Bicycle Motocross.

EXTRA ACTIVITY

Instead of getting a lift in a car, ride your bike to somewhere you normally get driven to e.g. school, shop or your friend's home.

CROSSWORD

Can you figure out the answers to these bicycle related clues and fill out the crossword?

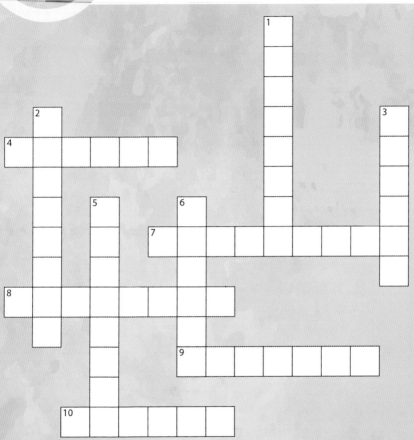

Across
4 A bike for two
7 A cycling racing track
8 Bike with one wheel
9 One wheel bike trick
10 A hard protective hat

Down
1 Curved strip over wheel
2 Early type of bike, Penny........
3 Wire rods on wheels
5 A small hole in a tyre
6 Colour of leaders jersey

52

ADVENTURE SNAP

BUCKETEER CODE
- Wear a helmet and hi-viz
- Keep to the left
- Look behind & give proper signal before moving off or making a turn
- Follow the rules of the road

Declaration
of challenge completion

I _____ declare that I have completed this challenege and I'm one step further to becoming a Bucketeer!

Who was with you when you completed this challenge?

_____

_____

_____

What happened during this challenge?

_____

_____

_____

_____

_____

Where did you complete this challenge?

_____

_____

How many stars do you rate this challenege? (Shade them in.)

☆ ☆ ☆ ☆ ☆

Witnessed by

Insert sticker here.

Date

_____   __ /__ /____

DAM A STREAM

Water in its natural habitat is always an amazing opportunity for fun! Just be extra careful as water is a powerful force of nature.

Find a stream, preferably ankle deep and about 1 metre wide.

Place a row of stones across the stream. Put the larger stones down first. Be extra careful not to hurt yourself while lifting.

Next place a second row of stones on top of the first. Ask an adult to help you.

Place twigs, leaves, branches or clay in front of the stones. The stones will hold them in place.

Look out for leaks in your dam and try to plug them.

DID YOU KNOW?

One of the tallest dams in the world is the 300m high Nurek Dam in Tajikistan.

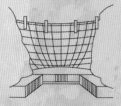 The Hoover Dam is a massive concrete dam, constructed on the Colorado River in the 1930s. There were 112 deaths associated with the construction of the dam.

Beaver dams are dams built by beavers to provide ponds as protection against predators and to provide easy access to food during winter.

Hydroelectric power, mostly from dams, supplies approximately 19% of the world's electricity.

One of the engineering wonders of the ancient world was the Great Dam of Marib in Yemen.

EXTRA ACTIVITY

Look out for 'pond skaters' and other insects that come to live in your newly created habitat.

COLOUR SUDOKU

To solve a Sudoku fill in the numbers 1 - 9 so that each number appears only once in each row going across, each coloumn going down and in each block of nine small squares.

In this puzzle there are also nine different colours, each with nine squares, and the numbers 1 - 9 must appear only once in each colour.

	8	1			6			
					9	3	1	6
4			7					5
5			3		8	6		
	7		2		4		9	
	2	3	5					7
9			1					8
2	4	6	8					
			3			6	5	

BUCKETEER'S CODE
Remember to have fun smashing down your dam when finished and leave the stream exactly as you found it.

ADVENTURE SNAP

Declaration
of challenge completion

I _____ declare that I have completed this challenege and I'm one step further to becoming a Bucketeer!

Who was with you when you completed this challenge?

_____

_____

What happened during this challenge?

_____

_____

_____

_____

Where did you complete this challenge?

_____

_____

How many stars do you rate this challenege? (Shade them in.)

☆ ☆ ☆ ☆ ☆

Witnessed by

Insert sticker here.

Date

_____   __ /__ /_____

MINI OLYMPICS

'Let the games begin!' There's no need to wait for every four years to savour the excitement of the Olympics, head outside and create your own record breaking attempts!

STEPS TO COMPLETION

 All participants must make the flag of the country that they will be representing.

 Play music and have an opening ceremony where everyone holds their flag whilst parading around.

 Choose what games will be included in your Mini Olympics: shotput, high jump, long jump, races, javelin, hurdles or discus.

 Use a notepad to keep account of 1st, 2nd & 3rd place in each event.

 Present medals and hold a closing ceremony to conclude the games.

DID YOU KNOW?

The ancient Olympic Games were held in Olympia, Greece from the 8th BC to the 4th century AD.

The five Olympic rings represent the five major regions of the world – Africa, the Americas, Asia, Europe and Oceania.

Baron Pierre de Coubertin founded the International Olympic Committee (IOC) in 1894, leading to the first modern Games in Athens in 1896.

American swimmer Michael Phelps (b.1985) has won the most Olympic medals with 28 medals (23 gold, 3 silver, 2 bronze).

Every national flag in the world includes one of the five Olympic ring colours, which are (from left to right) blue, yellow, black, green and red.

EXTRA ACTIVITY

Make gold, silver and bronze medals using clay and paint or card and markers.

FACT FINDING MISSION

Time to test your Olympic knowledge. Research the following famous people in sporting history and try to match them to the flag of their home country.

 ○

○ **FANNY BLANKERS-KOEN**
Find out about 'The Flying Housewife'.

 ○

○ **OSCAR SWAHN**
Find out why Oscar Swahn is a famous olympian.

 ○

○ **CASSIUS CLAY**
Find out about Cassius Clay, who won gold for boxing in 1960.

 ○

○ **USAIN BOLT**
Find out about Usain Bolt, the fastest man in history.

 ○

○ **NADIA COMANECI**
Find out about 14-year-old Nadia Comaneci at the 1976 Montreal Olympics.

ADVENTURE SNAP

Research local clubs in your area and try out a new sport. Who knows you might one day be a true Olympian!

Declaration
of challenge completion

I _____ declare that I have completed this challenege and I'm one step further to becoming a Bucketeer!

Who was with you when you completed this challenge?

_____

_____

What happened during this challenge?

_____

_____

_____

_____

Where did you complete this challenge?

_____

_____

How many stars do you rate this challenege? (Shade them in.)

☆   ☆   ☆   ☆   ☆

Witnessed by

Insert sticker here.

Date

_____   __ / __ / ____

66

FLY A KITE

Let your imagination soar as you marvel at the magic of flight with you at the controls! To complete this challenge all you need is your kite, some space and a windy day!

STEPS TO COMPLETION

You will need plenty of open space and a windy day!

Face away from the wind and hold up your kite, letting it catch the wind.

As the wind lifts the kite, let the line out.

If the wind slows or lulls, reel some line back in to steady your kite.

A steady tension on the line will keep your kite flying evenly.

DID YOU KNOW?

Kites were originally invented in China.

In Vietnam, kites are flown without tails. Instead small flutes are attached allowing the wind to 'hum' a musical tune.

'Kite fighting' is popular in many Asian countries, in which participants try to snag each other's kites or cut other kites down.

In 1750 Benjamin Franklin allegedly published a proposal for an experiment to prove that lightning was caused by electricity by flying a kite in a storm.

Weifang, Shandong, China is the kite capital of the world and is home to the world's largest kite museum.

EXTRA ACTIVITY

Record your 'air-time' to see if you can keep your kite flying for over 1 minute. Then try to beat your record!

KITE MAZE

Set this kite a flight by finding your way through the maze from the handle to the kite.

70

BUCKETEER'S CODE
- Keep clear of power lines, roads and aerials.
- Never fly kites near powerlines or in the path of traffic

ADVENTURE SNAP

Declaration
of challenge completion

I _____ declare that I have completed this challenege and I'm one step further to becoming a Bucketeer!

Who was with you when you completed this challenge?

_____

_____

What happened during this challenge?

_____

_____

_____

_____

Where did you complete this challenge?

_____

_____

How many stars do you rate this challenege? (Shade them in.)

☆ ☆ ☆ ☆ ☆

Witnessed by   Insert sticker here.   Date

_____   __/__/____

CONKER COMBAT

You must seek out a Horse Chestnut tree this autumn in order to complete this challenge. Look for a tree with leaves like the one Finn is holding. On the ground below you will find horse chestnuts (conkers).

STEPS TO COMPLETION

Ask an adult to help you make a hole in a large, hard conker using a nail, needle or electric drill.

A piece of string, about 20cm long, is threaded through it. Tie a large knot at one end of the string to secure the conker.

The game is played between two people, each with a conker.

One player lets the conker hang on the full length of the string while the other player swings their conker and hits.

Take turns hitting each other's conker until one conker breaks.

DID YOU KNOW?

The first recorded game of Conkers, using horse chestnuts, was played in 1848 on the Isle of Wight.

An earlier version of the game was played with snail shells or hazelnuts.

In 1965 the World Conker Championships (WCC) were set up in Northamptonshire, England, and still takes place on the second Sunday of October every year.

In 2001 Eamonn Dooley from Ireland broke the world record by smashing 306 conkers in one hour.

In 2004 several schools banned conkers due to fear of causing anaphylactic shock in pupils with nut allergies.

EXTRA ACTIVITY

'On your mark, get set, go!' Get some friends together and use the conkers you collected to have a conker and spoon race.

MAKE A CONKER WORM

Collect some conkers and lets get crafty! To create this conker worm you will need:

15 conkers
1 large one

googly eyes
& glue

drill or nail

string and a
blunt needle

1. Ask an adult to use a drill or a nail to put holes through each of the conkers you have collected.

2. Cut a long length of string and tie a knot at one end. Using a blunt needle, thread the string through the conkers leaving the largest one last (this will be the head).

3. Once you have added the final large conker to the string, tie a knot to secure it. Using the glue, stick the googly eyes onto the large conker to form the face.

ADVENTURE SNAP

Try to track these three trees. Oak for its little acorns, Sycamore for its helicopter wings and Blackthorn for its sour sloes.

Declaration
of challenge completion

I _____ declare that I have completed this challenege and I'm one step further to becoming a Bucketeer!

Who was with you when you completed this challenge?

_____

_____

_____

What happened during this challenge?

_____

_____

_____

_____

_____

Where did you complete this challenge?

_____

_____

How many stars do you rate this challenege? (Shade them in.)

☆ ☆ ☆ ☆ ☆

Witnessed by

_____

Insert sticker here.

Date

__ /__ /_____

CAMP OUT

Give your bed the heave ho, grab your tent and let's go! To complete this challenge you will need a fellow Bucketeer to share the experience of sleeping under the stars!

STEPS TO COMPLETION

Find a suitably flat location for your tent. Just make sure it is a safe and secure spot.

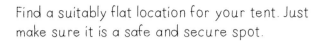
Pitch your tent in the daylight as its easier to see what you are doing.

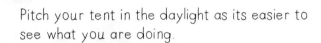
Make sure to bring adequate warm clothes, a pillow and a sleeping bag.

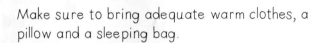
Bring some goodies for a midnight snack.

A torch is essential to light your way and to aid the telling of spooky stories.

DID YOU KNOW?

The term camp comes from the Latin word campus, meaning 'field'.

Antarctic explorers stayed in tents on their race to be first to The South Pole where temperatures reached as low as -89 degrees celcius.

Everest Base camp is in the lap of world highest mountain, Mount Everest, it is at an altitude of 5,364m from the sea level.

The world's largest tent is in Kazakhstan. The Khan Shatyr, is 150m high and has an area of 100,000 sq metre.

A Yurt is a circular tent of felt or skins on a collapsible framework, used by nomads in Mongolia, Siberia, and Turkey.

EXTRA ACTIVITY

See who is brave enough to get up in the middle of the night and run around the tent twice in the dark with no light to guide you (mind the pegs)!

LEARN THIS CAMPING SONG

This Land Is Your Land by Woody Guthrie

Chorus:
This land is your land, this land is my land,
From California to the New York Island;
From the Redwood forest to the Gulf Stream waters,
This land was made for you and Me.

As I was walking that ribbon of highway,
I saw above me that endless skyway,
I saw below me that golden valley,
This land was made for you and me.

Chorus

I roamed and I rambled and I followed my footsteps,
To the sparkling sands of her diamond deserts;
And all around me a voice was sounding,
This land was made for you and me.

Chorus

Take a look at the night sky and see if you can see any of these star constellations, The Plough, Orion or even the North Star!

ADVENTURE SNAP

Declaration
of challenge completion

I _____ declare that I have completed this challenege and I'm one step further to becoming a Bucketeer!

Who was with you when you completed this challenge?

_____

_____

What happened during this challenge?

_____

_____

_____

_____

Where did you complete this challenge?

_____

_____

How many stars do you rate this challenege? (Shade them in.)

☆ ☆ ☆ ☆ ☆

Witnessed by

Insert sticker here.

Date

_____   __/__/____

MAKE A MUD PIE

Bake someone happy! Ok Bucketeer to complete this challenge you're gonna get your hands dirty and sticky as you create muddy masterpieces!

Steps to Completion

 You will need: a bucket or old bowl or basin, clay, water, mixing-stick, flowers.

 Place your 'ingredients' into your bowl/bucket/basin.

 Mix well together, squeezing the mud through your fingers.

 Add water to the clay to make a good muddy texture.

 Mould the mixture into the shape of a pie and decorate the top with some leaves or flowers.

DID YOU KNOW?

Mud is a mixture of water and any combination of different kinds of soil.

Animals, such as hippopotamuses, pigs, rhinoceroses, water buffalo and elephants, bathe in mud in order to cool off and protect themselves from the sun.

Mud can be made into mud bricks, also called adobe, by mixing mud with water, placing the mixture into moulds and then allowing it to dry in open air.

Albuquerque, New Mexico, in the USA, hold a yearly event in which participants play volleyball in a giant mud pit.

A mud bath is a bath of mud, commonly from areas where hot spring water can combine with volcanic ash.

EXTRA ACTIVITY

Make some mud balls (same as snow balls) pick a target and aim.

SPOT THE DIFFERENCE

Can you spot the difference between the two mud-pies? See if you can find all six of them.

ADVENTURE SNAP

Try cooking for real in the kitchen with an adult! Cooking is a life skill and more importantly it is fun to share what you've baked with family and friends!

Declaration
of challenge completion

I _____ declare that I have completed this challenege and I'm one step further to becoming a Bucketeer!

Who was with you when you completed this challenge?

_____

_____

What happened during this challenge?

_____

_____

_____

_____

Where did you complete this challenge?

_____

_____

How many stars do you rate this challenege? (Shade them in.)

☆   ☆   ☆   ☆   ☆

Witnessed by   Insert sticker here.   Date

_____   __ /__ /____

CRAB FISHING

Let's go crabbing! It's just like fishing but without the fish, rod or nasty hook! After this activity our little crabbie cousins will be side-walking safely back to their home.

STEPS TO COMPLETION

Find a suitable spot on a harbour wall or at a big rock by the sea.

Tie a piece of bacon rind onto the end of a piece of string, drop the line into the water and wait!

Raise the string when you feel a tug on the line.

Place the crabs in a bucket of sea water.

Return them to the sea when you're finished examining them.

DID YOU KNOW?

Crabs live in all the world's oceans, in fresh water, and on land.

  They are generally covered with a thick exoskeleton and have a single pair of claws.

Crabs produce nearly 200,000 eggs which the female carries on her legs.

Crabs typically walk sideways.

Crabs are often boiled alive. In 2005 Norwegian scientists concluded that crustaceans could not feel pain.

EXTRA ACTIVITY

Try catch as many crabs as possible and release them a few metres from the water's edge and see which crab wins the race home.

WORD MAKER

There are more than 400 words hidden in the word 'CRUSTACEAN' how many can you find?

SCAR

NATURE

CRUSTACEAN

CREST

ARC

| T | R | A | C | E | | | | | | | |

CRAB CAKES INGREDIENTS

1 cup bread crumbs,
2 onions, finely chopped
1/4 cup finely chopped
sweet red pepper
1 large egg, lightly beaten

1/4 cup mayonnaise
1 tablespoon lemon juice
1/2 teaspoon garlic powder
400g of crabmeat
1 tablespoon butter

In a large bowl, combine bread crumbs, onions, red pepper, egg, mayonnaise, lemon juice, garlic powder and fold in the crab. Divide mixture into eight portions; shape into evenly sized (about the size of a hamburger) crab cakes. In a large nonstick pan, heat olive oil over medium-high heat. Add crab cakes; cook 3-4 minutes on each side or until golden brown.

Seafood is brain food! We should try to eat more of it so why not try this crab cake recipe with an adult.

ADVENTURE SNAP

Declaration
of challenge completion

I _____ declare that I have completed this challenege and I'm one step further to becoming a Bucketeer!

Who was with you when you completed this challenge?

_____

_____

_____

What happened during this challenge?

_____

_____

_____

_____

_____

Where did you complete this challenge?

_____

_____

How many stars do you rate this challenege? (Shade them in.)

☆ ☆ ☆ ☆ ☆

Witnessed by

Insert sticker here.

Date

_____   __ /__ /____

96

GROW YOUR OWN

Green fingers at the ready, it's time to get self-sufficient! Growing your own food can improve your health and is more delicious to eat, saves you money, helps the environment and is hugely satisfying!

STEPS TO COMPLETION

First you should decide what you would like to sow. Will it be vegetables, fruits or herbs?

You will need a pot/tray and some compost/soil to place seeds in.

Moisten the soil using a hose or watering can and place seeds in it.

Cover the seeds with more soil and water regularly.

When your crop is ripe, pick, wash and enjoy it.

DID YOU KNOW?

A strawberry is not an actual berry, but a banana is.

Apples float in water because they are 25% air.

The word potato comes from the spanish word 'patata'. Potatoes first appeared in Europe in 1586.

200 SEEDS

An average strawberry has around 200 seeds.

Kiwis were once known as Chinese gooseberries.

EXTRA ACTIVITY

Prepare a meal using the food you have grown.

WHICH GOES WHERE?

Can you categorise these 24 home grown foods into their correct patch of the garden?

Lemon
Peppers
Coriander
Peas
Oregano
Limes
Radish
Carrots
Strawberries
Chives
Grapes
Figs

Apricot
Parsley
Potatoes
Thyme
Olives
Papaya
Mint
Onions
Basil
Beans
Rosemary
Tomatoes

VEGETABLES

FRUITS

HERBS

ADVENTURE SNAP

Have a go at growing a sunflower. Remember to water your plant!

Declaration
of challenge completion

I _____ declare that I have completed this challenege and I'm one step further to becoming a Bucketeer!

Who was with you when you completed this challenge?

_____

_____

_____

What happened during this challenge?

_____

_____

_____

_____

_____

Where did you complete this challenge?

_____

_____

How many stars do you rate this challenege? (Shade them in.)

☆ ☆ ☆ ☆ ☆

Witnessed by

Insert sticker here.

Date

_____   __ / __ / ____

GARDEN PARTY

Roll up, roll up, it's party time! There'll be tasty treats, delicious drinks, music, dancing and good times to be had! Enjoy putting everything together to create the most awesome garden party ever!

STEPS TO COMPLETION

Make invitations and invite your guests to the garden party.

Decorate the garden with home made decorations and colourful balloons.

Create a playlist of fun summertime music.

Make some yummy treats for your guests.

Play some garden games, e.g. limbo, skittles, bowls, tag or musical statues.

DID YOU KNOW?

Long ago, gardens were essential to life. Early people were able to create towns and villages once they learned to plant their food, rather than moving from area to area gathering what they could find to eat.

 Every year the President of France holds a garden party at the Palais de l'Elysee in Paris on Bastille Day.

The legendary Hanging Gardens of Babylon were considered one of the Seven Wonders of the World. They were located in present-day Iraq.

Every summer, the Queen of England invites more than 30,000 people to Garden Parties at Buckingham Palace.

In the chapter 'A Mad Tea-Party' in Alice's Adventures in Wonderland, Alice becomes a guest at a tea party along with the March Hare, the Mad Hatter, and a sleeping Dormouse.

EXTRA ACTIVITY

Make a piñata and have fun smashing it to get the treats inside

CREATE A PARTY HAT

Make your party extra special with party hats! Get your arts and crafts materials together and create a personalised party hat for the garden party! For this activity you will need:

coloured card

marker, scissors & glue

stickers and craft set

a length of string

1. Mark out and cut off the corners of the card to form a circle. Then cut a narrow triangle starting from the outside to the center.

2. Fold the card to form a cone by overlapping the two bottom edges of the cut-out triangle. Apply glue to one edge of the cone and hold in place till dry.

3. Once dry, you can begin to decorate your party hat using any material you have at hand, such as stickers, jewels, glitter and shapes.

4. No party hat is complete without a fancy top! Decide what kind of top you would like on your hat... a fuzzy ball, coloured string maybe some crepe paper?

5. Cut two circular holes on each side of the bottom of the party hat. Then gather your string (measure length to fit head), and then tie knots on each side to secure.

ADVENTURE SNAP

Declaration
of challenge completion

I _____ declare that I have completed this challenege and I'm one step further to becoming a Bucketeer!

Who was with you when you completed this challenge?

_____

_____

What happened during this challenge?

_____

_____

_____

_____

Where did you complete this challenge?

_____

_____

How many stars do you rate this challenege? (Shade them in.)

☆ ☆ ☆ ☆ ☆

Witnessed by

Insert sticker here.

Date

__/__/____

SCAVENGER HUNT

Be careful where you walk, you could be stepping on a valid part of your challenge. Search high up and low down to find the hidden treasures all around you!

STEPS TO COMPLETION

A Scavenger Hunt can be held anywhere, e.g. in a garden, local park, beach or neighbourhood.

List the items that you need to find on your Scavenger Hunt. Give each person or team the list and a basket/bag or something to collect their items in.

Set a timer and decide on a finishing spot and finishing time.

The winner is the first person or team to find all the items on the list or the most items in the time frame.

Here is an example of items to put on your scavenger hunt list.

- 3 different leaves
- feather
- daisy
- something alive (Insect)

- a forked stick
- a round rock
- somthing red/black
- a piece of bark

110

DID YOU KNOW?

In Ancient times scavenger hunts were popular pastimes.

Vultures are one of the most well-known scavengers in the animal kingdom.

A scavenger hunt, is a search for a list of items in an area while a treasure hunt is when a series of clues leads you to a 'treasure'.

PROVO

The town of Provo in Utah has been entered into the Guinness Book of Records for organizing the world's largest scavenger hunt.

To search for and collect objects such as seashells and driftwood along the seashore is called 'Beachcombing'.

EXTRA ACTIVITY

Add a bonus item to the list (an object that would be very difficutl to find e.g, a snail's shell)

DICTIONARY HUNT

Grab a dictionary and go on an adventure through the English Language. Use a dictionary to find the following words. Fill in the answers and the page number you found them on.

1. THE LAST WORD DEFINED IN YOUR DICTIONARY

page

2. A WORD STARTING WITH X

page

3. A WORD WITH MORE THAN 3 MEANINGS

page

4. PICK A RANDOM PAGE AND WRITE THE LONGEST WORD ON THAT PAGE

page

5. A SILLY-SOUNDING WORD

page

7. A WORD WITH MORE THAN 3 SYLLABLES

page

8. IS YOUR NAME IN THE DICTIONARY? IF NOT, WHAT'S THE CLOSEST WORD TO YOUR NAME?

page

ADVENTURE SNAP

Ask an adult to set up a 'Treasure Hunt' with some fun clues and riddles that you must solve in order to discover your 'treasure'!

Declaration
of challenge completion

I _____ declare that I have completed this challenege and I'm one step further to becoming a Bucketeer!

Who was with you when you completed this challenge?

_____

_____

What happened during this challenge?

_____

_____

_____

_____

Where did you complete this challenge?

_____

_____

How many stars do you rate this challenege? (Shade them in.)

☆ ☆ ☆ ☆ ☆

Witnessed by

Insert sticker here.

Date

_____   __ /__ /_____

114

ROLL DOWN A HILL

Going up a hill can be really hard but coming down again can be 'wheely easy'. To complete this challenge you will need to find any suitable slope, the steeper the hill, the faster you'll roll!

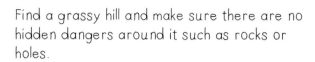

Find a grassy hill and make sure there are no hidden dangers around it such as rocks or holes.

Climb to the top then lay down with both arms close by your sides or outstretched.

Close your eyes and roll your way to the bottom.

To make this even more fun, include a friend. Lay down at the top of the hill, with your arms outstretched over your head. Get your friend to do the same.

Hold onto each other's outstretched hands and on the count of 3 roll down together.

DID YOU KNOW?

According to tradition, the Hill of Tara was the seat of the High King of Ireland.

 Ancient Rome was built on seven hills, protecting it from invaders.

Many settlements were originally built on hills, either to avoid floods or for defence. Hills offer a good view of the surrounding land and require would-be attackers to fight uphill.

Cheese rolling is an annual event in the West Country of England, which involves rolling a wheel of cheese down a hill. Contestants stand at the top and chase the wheel of cheese to the bottom.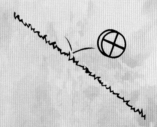

The largest manmade hill is in Sophienhohe, Germany (200 m).

EXTRA ACTIVITY

Try running down a really steep hill. Sand dunes are great for this.

WORDSEARCH

Find the names of these worldwide famous hills within the wordsearch below.

```
B D I E Z H I M A L A B
T Y G S A I P A N E M A
E R N Q Z M L Q T A E R
U R A U D H O L A R A N
F E R I F A I N D W Z A
E B I L U E R L E A V S
L K T I X K O A K E Y L
S C I N J I W N H C A I
B A T E H N V G O L E N
E H K E S C X I F T U G
R O L U V J A S O N M A
G A C H O C O L A T E N
```

Raudholar

Tadekho

Hackberry

Barnaslingan

Ipanema

Signal

Teufelsberg

Esquiline

Ezhimala

Chocolate

Oakey

Titirangi

Fantastic work, Bucketeer! Climbing hills can be hard work, remember to stay hydrated by drinking plenty of water.

ADVENTURE SNAP

Declaration
of challenge completion

I _____ declare that I have completed this challenege and I'm one step further to becoming a Bucketeer!

Who was with you when you completed this challenge?

_____

_____

_____

What happened during this challenge?

_____

_____

_____

_____

_____

Where did you complete this challenge?

_____

_____

How many stars do you rate this challenege? (Shade them in.)

☆ ☆ ☆ ☆ ☆

Witnessed by

Insert sticker here.

Date

_____   __ / __ / _____

120

JUMP OVER WAVES

Waves that began hundreds of kilometres out to sea come to a fun-filled end on the shore as you jump over the breakers navigating towards challenge completion!

STEPS TO COMPLETION

Best done on a windy day when waves are bigger. Ensure an adult is with you.

Pick out your wave of choice.

Time it so you jump just as its about to break.

Try to leave it as late as possible before you jump 'with' the wave.

Get back on your feet and prepare for the next wave.

DID YOU KNOW?

Ocean waves are caused by wind moving across the surface of the water.

Waves in the oceans can travel thousands of kilometres before reaching land.

The tallest wave ever measured was 1719 feet (524m) at Lituya Bay, Alaska in 1958.

The water doesn't travel with the wave, but only moves up and down.

The tallest wave recorded in the open ocean was 95 feet (29m) during a storm near Scotland.

EXTRA ACTIVITY

Jump over the waves with your eyes closed. Hold hands with your friends and jump together.

ADVENTURE SNAP

NO SWIMMING

BETWEEN TWO RED AND YELLOW FLAGS
safe to swim and belly board

BETWEEN TWO BLACK AND WHITE FLAGS
NO SWIMMING
area for surfers and windsurfers

Declaration
of challenge completion

I _____ declare that I have completed this challenege and I'm one step further to becoming a Bucketeer!

Who was with you when you completed this challenge?

_____

_____

What happened during this challenge?

_____

_____

_____

_____

Where did you complete this challenge?

_____

_____

How many stars do you rate this challenege? (Shade them in.)

☆   ☆   ☆   ☆   ☆

Witnessed by   Insert sticker here.   Date

_____   __/__/____

WATER FIGHT

Best enjoyed outdoors on a summer's day!
This challenge will have you run, hide, fall, aim,
shoot and get utterly drenched! A challenge
impossible to do without screaming with
laughter and howling with joy.

STEPS TO COMPLETION

Choose your location wisely, you will need access to a water supply (e.g. outdoor tap or a paddling pool).

Wear light clothes that will dry quickly or have spare clothes nearby.

Have your weapons at the ready (water guns, water balloons, garden hoses, bazookas, bottles, buckets anything that can carry water)!

Make sure there are no electrical items around that may get wet.

Champion is determined by level of wetness.

DID YOU KNOW?

Water is a transparent, tasteless, odourless and nearly colourless substance.

 WATER – 71%
LAND – 29%   Water covers 71% of the Earth's surface.

Water play is exhibited by other animals such as monkeys or even elephants opting to spray themselves and others in an attempt to cool off during hotter months.

The world's biggest water fight takes place every year at the Songkran Festival in Thailand.

APRIL
13/14/15
SONGKRAN
FESTIVAL

Only 2.5% of water is freshwater and 98.8% of that water is ice.

EXTRA ACTIVITY

Water tag: The person who is 'It' uses a water gun to tag players. Once you are tagged, you become 'It'.

PAPER WATER BALLOON TASK

Follow the instruction and create your very own paper water balloon.

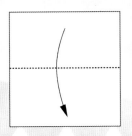

1. Fold in half.

2. Fold in half.

3. Open the ⇨ part.

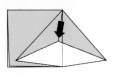

4. Flatten this space.

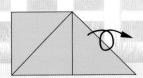

5. Turn over.

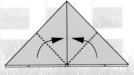

6. Open the ⇦ part.

7. Fold in the dotted lines to meet the centre line.

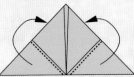

8. Fold backward in the dotted lines.

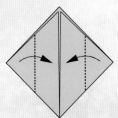

9. Fold in the dotted lines.

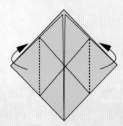

10. Fold backward in the dotted lines.

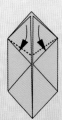

11. Tuck them into the pockets.

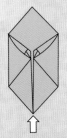

12. Blow up from ⇧

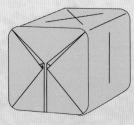

13. Finished. Now fill with water and throw!

130

Invite your friends for an Aqua Attack Adventure. In teams, try to get each other as wet as possible. Set a finishing time and award points at the end. 3 points for a wet player, 5 points for dripping clothes and 10 for a totally drenched player!

ADVENTURE SNAP

Declaration
of challenge completion

I _____ declare that I have completed this challenege and I'm one step further to becoming a Bucketeer!

Who was with you when you completed this challenge?

_____

_____

What happened during this challenge?

_____

_____

_____

_____

_____

Where did you complete this challenge?

_____

How many stars do you rate this challenege? (Shade them in.)

☆ ☆ ☆ ☆ ☆

Witnessed by

Insert sticker here.

Date

_____   __/__/____

132

BUILD AN OBSTACLE COURSE

Whoever knew that a boring old garden
could be turned into an arena of adventure!
A rollercoaster route of adrenalin as you
jump, crawl, hop, skip, slip, slide, roll and run
through your very own self-made obstacle
course.

Put a brush across two buckets and two chairs. You must jump over the bucket hurdle and crawl under the chair hurdle.

Make a tunnel by arranging chairs in a line and crawl through the legs.

Use a water pistol to shoot empty bottles out of a tree.

Make a balance beam by putting a plank of wood across two chairs and walk across from one to the other.

Throw tennis balls or rolled-up socks into a bucket from a set distance.

DID YOU KNOW?

Obstacle courses can include running, climbing, jumping, crawling, swimming and balancing elements with the aim of testing speed and endurance.

Show jumping is an obstacle course on horse back.

The game show, 'Wipeout' revolves around the objective of completing obstacle courses.

Elite forces in the military use obstacle courses as part of their training.

They are used to test stamina, grit, camaraderie, mental and physical strength.

EXTRA ACTIVITY

Use a stopwatch to time yourself and see who can complete the course in the fastest time.

OBSTACLE ORBS

Can you find the 5 hidden obstacle challenges?

136

ADVENTURE SNAP

Invite your friends over and challenge them to complete your unique obstacle course!

Declaration
of challenge completion

I _____ declare that I have completed this challenege and I'm one step further to becoming a Bucketeer!

Who was with you when you completed this challenge?

_____

_____

_____

What happened during this challenge?

_____

_____

_____

_____

_____

Where did you complete this challenge?

_____

_____

How many stars do you rate this challenege? (Shade them in.)

☆ ☆ ☆ ☆ ☆

Witnessed by   Insert sticker here.   Date

_____   __ /__ /____

HOOK
by Ayla and Finn

PERFORM A SHOW

Lights, Camera, Action!
For this challenge you can stage a play, a
puppet show, a comedy act, sing, dance,
mime, perform magic tricks, do gymnastics,
anything to showcase your talent.
'All the world's a stage.' William Shakespeare

STEPS TO COMPLETION

Decide on what your performance will be and give a script or instructions to all performers.

Practice until everyone feels confident enough to perform in front of an audience.

Gather or make any props your show may require. Decide on a show time.

Invite guests to attend your performance. Ensure there are enough chairs around the stage for your audience.

'Break a Leg!'

DID YOU KNOW?

If you say 'Macbeth' in a theatre, you are meant to walk three times in a circle anti-clockwise, then either spit or say a rude word.

An amphitheatre is an open-air venue used for entertainment, performances and sports. The Colosseum in Rome is the largest and most famous amphitheatre in the world.

Two seats are permanently left open at the Palace Theatre for the theatre ghosts to sit in.

Well-wishers typically say 'Break a leg' to actors and musicians before they go on stage to perform as saying 'good luck' is considered bad luck.

We can thank Shakespeare for inventing over 1,700 of the words that we still use to this day.

EXTRA ACTIVITY

'Hot Seating' Get into character and ask the audience if they have any questions. Take on the role of the character you are playing while answering their questions.

MAKE SHADOW PUPPETS

Light can only travel in straight lines so when you put an object in front of the light you create a shadow. Try to make these puppet animals:

- Use a torch or lamp to shine a light on a bare wall. It works best if the room is dark.

- To make these animal shadows you must put your hands in the positions shown below.

- Experiment to create your own weird and wonderful puppets.

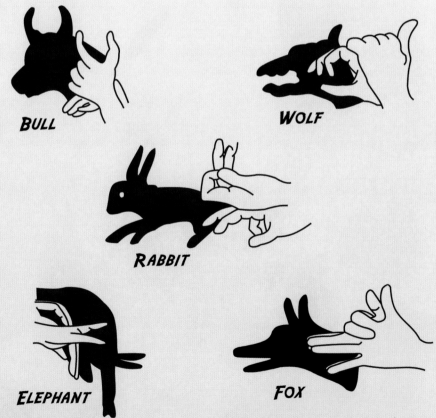

BULL

WOLF

RABBIT

ELEPHANT

FOX

142

Watch out for one of nature's most mesmerising performances. A murmuration of starlings is an amazing sight - a swooping mass of birds whirling in the sky above your head.

ADVENTURE SNAP

Declaration
of challenge completion

I _____ declare that I have completed this challenege and I'm one step further to becoming a Bucketeer!

Who was with you when you completed this challenge?

_____

_____

What happened during this challenge?

_____

_____

_____

_____

_____

Where did you complete this challenge?

_____

_____

How many stars do you rate this challenege? (Shade them in.)

☆ ☆ ☆ ☆ ☆

Witnessed by

Insert sticker here.

Date

_____

__ / __ / _____

144

MAKE A SNOWMAN

There's no better way to begin the day,
pulling back the curtains to reveal a blanket
of white covering everything and being told
school is cancelled as it's a 'Snow-Day'

STEPS TO COMPLETION

Wrap up well; coats, hats, scarves, wellies and most importantly, gloves!

To make a snowman, start with a tightly squeezed snowball, roll it in a very snowy area (over grass is perfect) until it's the perfect size for a body.

Repeat this but make it smaller for the snowman's head.

Get some help to lift the head on to the body. Use extra snow to seal the head to the body.

Gather some old clothes (hat, scarf), get sticks for his arms, coal for his buttons and a carrot for his nose!

DID YOU KNOW?

An avalanche is a rapid flow of snow down a sloping surface.

Guinness World Records list the world's largest snowflakes as those of January 1887 at Fort Keogh, Montana. Allegedly one measured 38 cm wide.

The world record for the highest total snowfall was measured in the US at Mount Baker, in Washington during the 1998–1999 season. It received 2,896 cm of snow.

190MPH

An avalanche can exceed speeds of 300 kilometres per hour, and masses of 10,000,000 tonnes.

31 January 2016 in Saskatoon, Canada, more than 7,681 people took part to set the new world record for the world's largest snowball fight!

EXTRA ACTIVITY

Make a snow family, snow dog and perhaps a snow house or igloo.

147

CRACK THE CODE

Complete these sums in order to crack the code and reveal the hidden message.

CRACK THE CODE

S = (65+83)-92   T = (87+36)-63
W = (74+96)-65   Y = (84+35)-26
A = (95-63)+32   E = (57-21)+19
R = (89-27)+13   L = (56-38)+22
O = (233+105)-66   V = (409+326)-44
N = (508+365)-99

774	55	691	55	75

55	64	60

93	55	40	40	272	105

56	774	272	105

ADVENTURE SNAP

The snow won't last forever so get out there, have a snowball fight, go sledging, make snow angels, make a sleigh and play with your friends!

Declaration
of challenge completion

I _____ declare that I have completed this challenege and I'm one step further to becoming a Bucketeer!

Who was with you when you completed this challenge?

_____

_____

What happened during this challenge?

_____

_____

_____

_____

Where did you complete this challenge?

_____

_____

How many stars do you rate this challenege? (Shade them in.)

☆　　☆　　☆　　☆　　☆

Witnessed by　　　　　Insert sticker here.　　　　　Date

_____　　　　　　　　　　__/__/_____

150

When you have finished a challenge place the matching sticker on to the Declaration of Completion for that challenge.

Insert sticker here.

When you have finished each challenge place the matching sticker of the challenge on to the final Certificate of Completion.

Certi
of com

It is hereb

is a fun-loving, adventure-chasing, t
Awa

Finn Finn _____ Ayla

ficate
pletion

certified that

_____

hrill-seeking, fully-fledged Bucketeer.
ded by;

Ayla _____ Date __/__/____